INTRODUCTION

Practical Musicianship replaced General Musicianship with effect from January 1990. It has been designed: to cover all grades; to apply to all instrumentalists and singers (and not only to candidates with a keyboard facility); and to provide a suitable alternative exemption to Grade 5 Theory for entry to Grades 6-8 of all Practical subjects.

Candidates will be expected to use the piano or an instrument of their own choice, providing it is one which is included in the current range of subjects offered in the Board's syllabuses.

Where applicable, tests will be played by the examiner on the piano.

Candidates may, where appropriate, sing tests on 'lah' or any other vowel sound or to sol-fa as they prefer.

GRADE 1

1A To tap, as an echo, the rhythm-pattern of two two-bar phrases in simple time played by the examiner. The echoes should follow each phrase in strict time without an intervening pause.

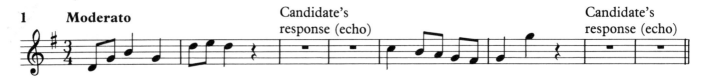

1B To sing, as an echo, two two-bar phrases in simple time played by the examiner. The echoes should follow each phrase in strict time without an intervening pause.

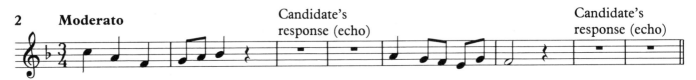

1C To play from memory on an instrument chosen by the candidate a two-bar melody played twice by the examiner. The key-chord and starting note will first be sounded and named. The examiner will choose a key and pitch suitable for the candidate's instrument.

1D To sing at sight a four-bar melody in 2/4 time. A simple accompaniment will be played by the examiner. The key-chord and starting note will first be sounded and named.

AB 2044

1E To improvise with voice or instrument, at the choice of the candidate, a two-bar answering phrase to a two-bar phrase played by the examiner. The key-chord will first be sounded and named. The answering phrase should follow in strict time after the examiner has played the opening phrase. The examiner will choose a key and pitch suitable for the candidate's instrument. A second attempt will be allowed.

1F To recognize, from the printed score, the three or four changes made to pitch and note-values in a melody played twice by the examiner. The candidate will be required to point to and explain the differences. The key-chord will be sounded before the melody is played.

CANDIDATE'S COPY

EXAMINER PLAYS

CANDIDATE'S COPY

EXAMINER PLAYS

GRADE 2

2A To sing, as an echo, two two-bar phrases in simple time played by the examiner, whilst continuously tapping a repeated rhythm-pattern (i.e. an ostinato) previously indicated by the examiner. The echoes should follow each phrase in strict time without an intervening pause.

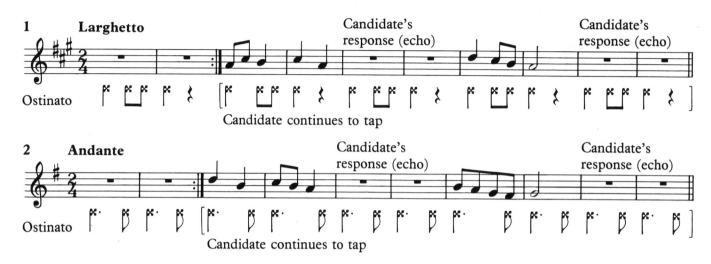

2B To play from memory on an instrument chosen by the candidate a two-bar melody played twice by the examiner. The key-chord and starting note will first be sounded and named. The examiner will choose a key and pitch suitable for the candidate's instrument.

2C To sing at sight a four-bar melody in 2/4 or 3/4 time. A simple accompaniment will be played by the examiner. The key-chord and starting note will first be sounded and named.

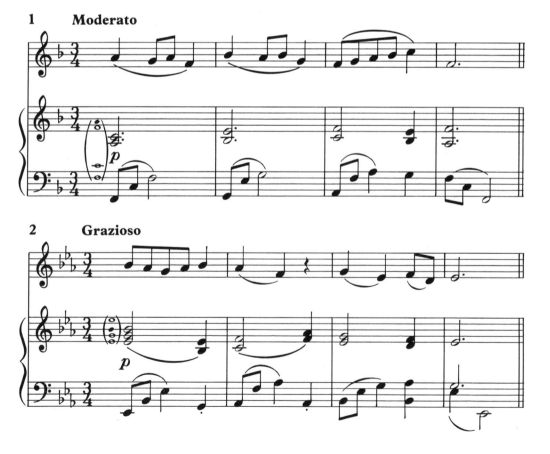

2D To improvise with voice or instrument, at the choice of the candidate, a two-bar answering phrase to a two-bar phrase played by the examiner. The key-chord will first be sounded and named. The answering phrase should follow in strict time after the examiner has played the opening phrase. The examiner will choose a key and pitch suitable for the candidate's instrument. A second attempt will be allowed.

2E To recognize, from the printed score, the three or four changes made to pitch and note-values in a melody played twice by the examiner. The candidate will be required to point to and explain the differences. The key-chord will be sounded before the melody is played.

CANDIDATE'S COPY

EXAMINER PLAYS

CANDIDATE'S COPY

EXAMINER PLAYS

GRADE 3

3A   To sing, as an echo, two two-bar phrases in simple time played by the examiner, whilst continuously tapping a repeated rhythm-pattern (i.e. an ostinato) previously indicated by the examiner. The echoes should follow each phrase in strict time without an intervening pause.

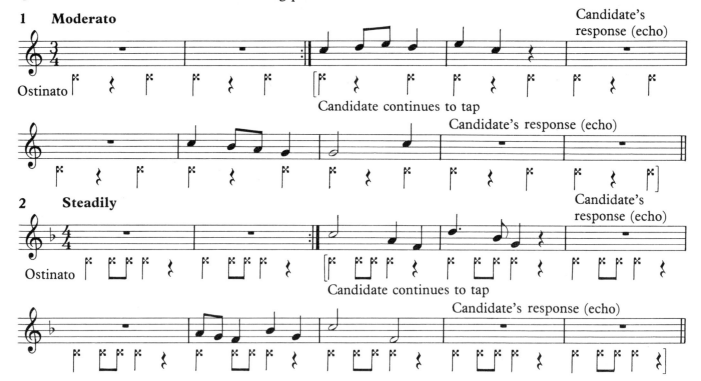

3B   To play from memory on an instrument chosen by the candidate a two-bar melody played twice by the examiner. The key-chord and starting note will first be sounded and named. The examiner will choose a key and pitch suitable for the candidate's instrument.

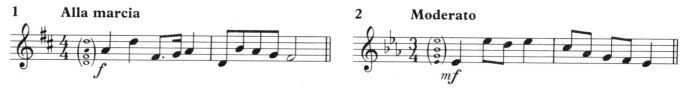

3C   To sing at sight a four-bar melody in 2/4, 3/4, 4/4 or 6/8 time. An accompaniment will be played by the examiner. The key-chord and starting note will first be sounded and named.

3D To improvise with voice or instrument, at the choice of the candidate, a four-bar answering phrase to a four-bar phrase played by the examiner. The key-chord will first be sounded and named. The answering phrase should follow in strict time after the examiner has played the opening phrase. The examiner will choose a key and pitch suitable for the candidate's instrument. A second attempt will be allowed.

3E To recognize, from the printed score, the four changes made to pitch, note- and rest-values and dynamics in a melody played twice by the examiner. The candidate will be required to point to and explain the differences. The key-chord will be sounded before the melody is played.

GRADE 4

4A To **sing** from memory a four-bar melody in 2/4 or 3/4 time played twice by the examiner. The key-chord and starting note will first be sounded and named. The examiner will then play the melody a third time and the candidate will be required to **play** it from memory on an instrument of his/her choice. The examiner will choose a key and pitch suitable for the instrument.

1 **Allegretto**

2 **Allegretto**

4B To sing at sight the lower part of a two-part passage of two bars length while the examiner plays the upper part. The key-chord and starting note will first be sounded and the pulse indicated.

1 **Andante**

2 **Con spirito**

4C To sing at sight a short melody in 2/4, 3/4, 4/4 or 6/8 time. An accompaniment will be played by the examiner. The key-chord and starting note will first be sounded.

Slow

4D To improvise with voice or instrument, at the choice of the candidate, an extension to the given opening of a short melody over a simple accompaniment played by the examiner. The implied harmonic scheme will be confined to chords of the tonic and dominant. In the examination the candidate will be given a score showing the melody opening in different keys and with different clefs to accommodate the full range of instruments, and the chord symbols of the accompaniment. A second attempt will be allowed.

Allegretto

4E To recognize, from the printed score, the four changes which may include pitch, rhythm, dynamics and tempo, in a short piano piece played twice by the examiner. Changes to notes and rhythm will be confined to the melodic line. The candidate will be required to point to and explain the differences.

CANDIDATE'S COPY

Leopold Mozart

EXAMINER PLAYS

GRADE 5

5A   To **sing** from memory a four-bar melody in 2/4, 3/4, 4/4 or 6/8 time played twice by the examiner. The key-chord and starting note will first be sounded and named. The examiner will then play the melody a third time and the candidate will be required to **play** it from memory on an instrument of his/her choice. The examiner will choose a key and pitch suitable for the instrument.

1   Moderato

2   Ritmico

5B1   The candidate may choose: (1) to transpose at sight on the chosen instrument a four-bar melody up or down a tone or semitone. A key suitable for the candidate's instrument will be given.

5B2   **or** (2) to sing at sight the lower part of a four-bar phrase while the examiner plays the upper part. The key-chord and starting note will first be sounded and the pulse indicated.

1   Andante

2   Doloroso

5C To sing or play at sight, at the choice of the candidate, a short melody including the realization of dynamics, simple ornamentation (except when the test is sung), and the more common marks of expression. Candidates will be allowed a preliminary attempt before being assessed. The key-chord and starting note will first be sounded if the test is sung, and the words provided need not be used.

1 **Minuet** Haydn (adapted)

2 **Andante** de Fesch

3 **Largo** Bishop

Sleep gen - tle La - dy, the flow'rs are clo - sing. The

ve - ry winds and waves re - po - - - - sing.

5D1 The candidate may choose: (1) to improvise with voice or instrument, at the choice of the candidate, an extension to a melody over an accompaniment played by the examiner. The implied harmonic scheme will be confined to chords of the tonic, dominant, subdominant and supertonic of major keys of not more than two sharps or one flat. In the examination the candidate will be given a score showing the melody opening in different keys and with different clefs to accommodate the full range of instruments, and the chord symbols of the accompaniment. A second attempt will be allowed.

Moderato

5D2 **or** (2) to improvise at the keyboard an accompaniment to a given melody which will be annotated with chord symbols. The harmonic scheme will be within the limitations stated in (1) above. A suggested but optional opening will be provided. The examiner will play the melody, if requested to do so, while the candidate plays the accompaniment, or the candidate may incorporate the melody in the accompaniment. Candidates will be given credit for the effective use of inversions of the chords.

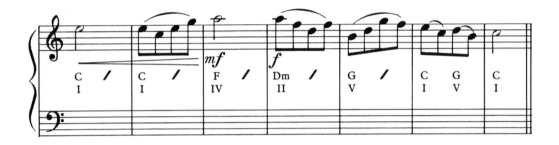

5E To perform a short free improvisation based on a given motif or interval chosen by the examiner. The examiner will look for imaginative use of the given material, effective use of the voice or instrument and a sense of structure.

5F   To recognize, from the printed score, the five changes, which may include pitch, rhythm, dynamics, tempo, articulation and phrasing, in a short piano piece played twice by the examiner. Changes to notes and rhythm will be confined to the melodic line. The candidate will be required to point to and explain the differences.

CANDIDATE'S COPY

EXAMINER PLAYS

ABRSM PUBLISHING

The Associated Board of
the Royal Schools of Music
(Publishing) Limited

14 Bedford Square
London WC1B 3JG

ISBN 1-85472-417-7

9 781854 724175